BONI LONNSBURRY

gratitude
journal

A Magical Place to
Multiply Your Blessings

InnerArt®
Making your inner art magnificent

Inner Art, Inc.

530 Compton Street #D, Broomfield, CO 80020

www.InnerArtInc.com

Editor: Bryna Haynes, TheAuthorRevolution.com
Cover design and Interior layout: Rachel Dunham and Heather McNamara, YourBrandTherapy.com

Ordering Information

Quantity sales. Special discounts are available on quantity purchases by corporations, associations, and others. For details, please contact the publisher at the address above.

ISBN: 978-1-941322-19-2

1. Nonfiction > Self-Help > Personal Growth > Success
2. Nonfiction > Body, Mind & Spirit > New Thought

table of contents

table of *contents*

table of *contents*

Hello *grateful* being!

Gratitude is far more than saying, *"Thank you."* Feeling genuinely grateful sends out a siren call to the universe that shouts, *"I love this, I appreciate this, and want more of it!"* Feeling grateful–really, truly and deeply grateful–works magic. It becomes an energy that literally creates more things to feel grateful for.

In this journal you will list three things that happened recently that you're grateful for. They can be little things or big things, but go beyond the simple list. Take a moment to elaborate on at least one thing on that list. Write the details of that gratitude.

For example, *"I am grateful for the sunset I witnessed tonight. Yellows, reds and purples splashed across the sky as the sun forced its way through a patchwork of clouds. Its beauty made me shiver, and I felt, in that moment, as if I were touched by God."*

It doesn't have to be poetic or well written. But if you write about the details of what you experienced and especially how you *felt*, you will strengthen the *power* of your gratitude.

You'll also write about something in your life that you are grateful for. Again, go into some detail here and feel the appreciation deeply as you write.

Then you'll write about something that happened in the past that you feel grateful to have experienced. Maybe it was a difficult lesson but you grew, perhaps it was a mentor or friend who made a difference in your life, or it could be an experience you had that touched you in some way. It doesn't have to be big or profound—it could be the memory of warm bologna and mayo sandwiches you looked forward to for lunch in third grade.

To add to the creative cocoon of positive vibes, you'll write about something from the future that you will be grateful for. Write as if you already have this dream. Feel the deliciousness of this blessing in your life and let the gratitude wash over you. Feel the energies of triumph and celebration.

Lastly, you'll write about (or simply read, if this is written for you) one of your eternal blessings. These are blessings of a more spiritual nature.

Use this journal on a regular basis—and you will transform your life.

with love,

Boni

p.s.

When your gratitudes manifest into successes (little or big), please let us know! Your success inspires others! Visit

LiveALifeYouLove.com/ Inspire/#Simple2

"Thank you"
is the best prayer that
anyone could say.

*I say that one a lot. Thank you expresses
extreme gratitude, humility, understanding.*

- Alice Walker

Three things that happened today (or yesterday)
that I'm grateful for

....

....

....

....

....

....

....

....

....

....

....

....

....

Something in *my life* that I am grateful for

....
....
....
....
....
....

Something from *my past* that I am grateful for

....
....
....
....
....
....

One thing from
my future
that I *will* be grateful for

(something I am consciously creating and that I claim NOW)

One of my
eternal blessings

I am deeply grateful that I am
unconditionally loved by Source,
my soul, my spirit, and my higher self.

I don't have to chase

extraordinary moments
to find happiness-

*it's right in front of me if I'm paying
attention and practicing gratitude.*

- Brené Brown

Three things that happened today (or yesterday)
that I'm grateful for

Something in *my life* that I am grateful for

....

....

....

....

....

....

Something from *my past* that I am grateful for

....

....

....

....

....

One thing from
my future
that I *will* be grateful for

(something I am consciously creating and that I claim NOW) ....

....

....

....

....

....

....

....

....

....

....

....

....

....

One of my
eternal blessings

*Piglet noticed that even
though he had a very small heart,*
it could hold a rather
large amount
of gratitude.

- A.A. Milne in *Winnie-the-Pooh*

Three things that happened today (or yesterday)

that I'm grateful for

Something in *my life* that I am grateful for

....

....

....

....

....

....

Something from *my past* that I am grateful for

....

....

....

....

....

....

One thing from
my future
that I *will* be grateful for

(something I am consciously creating and that I claim NOW) ....

....

....

....

....

....

....

....

....

....

....

....

....

....

One of my
eternal blessings

I am thankful that
I create my entire reality.

Gratitude is the
sign of noble souls.

- Aesop

Three things that happened today (or yesterday)
that I'm grateful for

....

....

....

....

....

....

....

....

....

....

....

....

....

Something in *my life* that I am grateful for

....
....
....
....
....
....

Something from *my past* that I am grateful for

....
....
....
....
....

One thing from
my future
that I *will* be grateful for

(something I am consciously creating and that I claim NOW) ....

....

....

....

....

....

....

....

....

....

....

....

....

One of my
eternal blessings

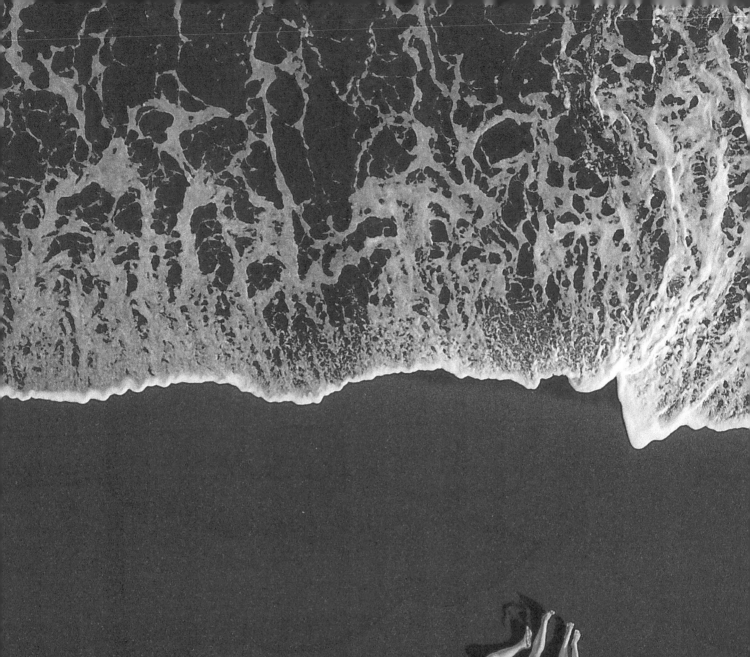

Showing gratitude
is one of the simplest
yet most powerful things
humans can do
for each other.

- Randy Pausch

Three things that happened today (or yesterday)
that I'm grateful for

....

....

....

....

....

....

....

....

....

....

....

....

....

....

Something in *my life* that I am grateful for

....

....

....

....

....

....

Something from *my past* that I am grateful for

....

....

....

....

....

....

One thing from *my future* that I *will* be grateful for

(something I am consciously creating and that I claim NOW) ....

....

....

....

....

....

....

....

....

....

....

....

....

....

....

One of my
eternal blessings

I am grateful that I am a
part, a piece, an immutable
bit of the divine.

If you want the
good to expand, begin
a ritual of gratitude.

Mentally list all the wonderful things about
someone you love every morning as you shower
—and watch the list grow.

- Boni Lonnsburry

Three things that happened today (or yesterday)

that I'm grateful for

....

....

....

....

....

....

....

....

....

....

....

....

....

....

Something in
my life
that I am grateful for

....
....
....
....
....
....

Something from
my past
that I am grateful for

....
....
....
....
....
....

One thing from
my future
that I *will* be grateful for

(something I am consciously creating and that I claim NOW) ....

....

....

....

....

....

....

....

....

....

....

....

....

....

One of my
eternal blessings

....

....

....

....

....

....

....

....

....

....

....

a thankful heart is not only the greatest virtue, but the parent of all other virtues.

– Marcus Cicero

Three things that happened today (or yesterday)
that I'm grateful for

....

....

....

....

....

....

....

....

....

....

....

....

....

....

Something in *my life* that I am grateful for

....

....

....

....

....

....

Something from *my past* that I am grateful for

....

....

....

....

....

One thing from *my future* that I *will* be grateful for

(something I am consciously creating and that I claim NOW) ....

....

....

....

....

....

....

....

....

....

....

....

....

....

One of my
eternal blessings

I love that I can simply
hold an intention and
the way will be shown.

When you practice
gratefulness

there is a sense of
respect
towards others.

– The Dalai Lama

Three things that happened today (or yesterday)
that I'm grateful for

Something in
my life
that I am grateful for

....

....

....

....

....

....

Something from
my past
that I am grateful for

....

....

....

....

....

....

One thing from *my future* that I *will* be grateful for

(something I am consciously creating and that I claim NOW) ....

....

....

....

....

....

....

....

....

....

....

....

....

....

....

One of my
eternal blessings

The essence of all
beautiful art,
all great art,
is gratitude.

-Friedrich Nietzsche

Three things that happened today (or yesterday)
that I'm grateful for

Something in *my life* that I am grateful for

....

....

....

....

....

....

Something from *my past* that I am grateful for

....

....

....

....

....

....

One thing from
my future that I *will* be grateful for

(something I am consciously creating and that I claim NOW) ....

....

....

....

....

....

....

....

....

....

....

....

....

....

....

One of my *eternal blessings*

I feel blessed that I am forgiven by God, Goddess, All That Is for the less than stellar things I've done.

silent gratitude isn't much use to anyone.

— Gertrude Stein

Three things that happened today (or yesterday)

that I'm grateful for

Something in *my life* that I am grateful for

....
....
....
....
....
....

Something from *my past* that I am grateful for

....
....
....
....
....

One thing from *my future* that I *will* be grateful for

(something I am consciously creating and that I claim NOW)

One of my
eternal blessings

Opportunities,
relationships, even
money flowed my way
when I learned
to be grateful
no matter what
happened in my life.

- Oprah Winfrey

Three things that happened today (or yesterday)

that I'm grateful for

Something in *my life* that I am grateful for

....

....

....

....

....

....

Something from *my past* that I am grateful for

....

....

....

....

....

....

One thing from
my future
that I *will* be grateful for

(something I am consciously creating and that I claim NOW) ....

....

....

....

....

....

....

....

....

....

....

....

....

....

One of my
eternal blessings

I am grateful for gratitude—a force
beyond my comprehension.

Oh Lord, that lends me life,
lend me a heart
replete with
thankfulness.

- **William Shakespeare**

Three things that happened today (or yesterday)

that I'm grateful for

....

....

....

....

....

....

....

....

....

....

....

....

....

....

Something in *my life* that I am grateful for

....
....
....
....
....
....

Something from *my past* that I am grateful for

....
....
....
....
....
....

One thing from
my future
that I *will* be grateful for

(something I am consciously creating and that I claim NOW) ....

....

....

....

....

....

....

....

....

....

....

....

....

....

....

One of my
eternal blessings

....

....

....

....

....

....

....

....

....

....

....

....

....

As we express our gratitude,
we must never forget that the
highest appreciation

is not to utter words,
but to live by them.

– John F. Kennedy

Three things that happened today (or yesterday)

that I'm grateful for

Something in *my life* that I am grateful for

....

....

....

....

....

....

Something from *my past* that I am grateful for

....

....

....

....

....

....

One thing from
my future
that I *will* be grateful for

(something I am consciously creating and that I claim NOW) ....

....

....

....

....

....

....

....

....

....

....

....

....

....

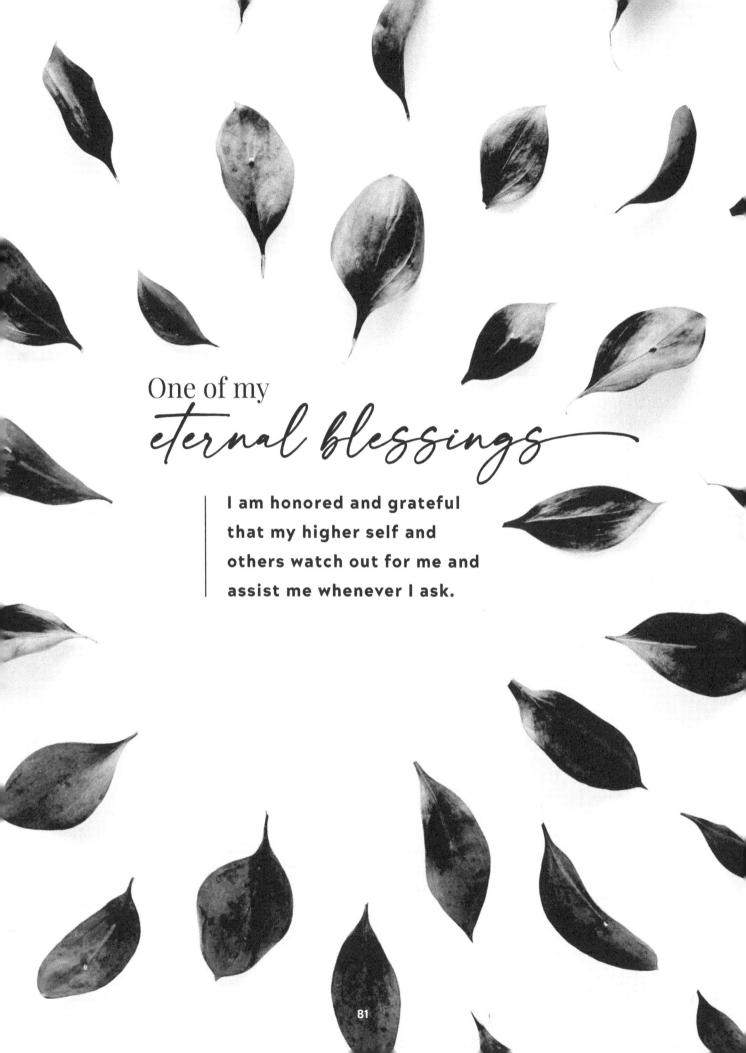

One of my
eternal blessings

I am honored and grateful
that my higher self and
others watch out for me and
assist me whenever I ask.

Feeling gratitude and
not expressing it is like
wrapping a present and

not giving it.

— William Arthur Ward

Three things that happened today (or yesterday) that I'm grateful for

Something in *my life* that I am grateful for

....

....

....

....

....

....

Something from *my past* that I am grateful for

....

....

....

....

....

....

One thing from
my future
that I *will* be grateful for

(something I am consciously creating and that I claim NOW) ....

....

....

....

....

....

....

....

....

....

....

....

....

....

One of my
eternal blessings

thankfulness
is the beginning of
gratitude.

gratitude
is the completion of
thankfulness.

Thankfulness may
consist merely of words.
*gratitude is
shown in acts.*

- Henri Frederic

Three things that happened today (or yesterday)

that I'm grateful for

....

....

....

....

....

....

....

....

....

....

....

....

....

....

Something in *my life* that I am grateful for

....

....

....

....

....

....

Something from *my past* that I am grateful for

....

....

....

....

....

....

One thing from *my future* that I *will* be grateful for

(something I am consciously creating and that I claim NOW)

One of my
eternal blessings

I am thankful that I have the power and ability to forgive myself and others.

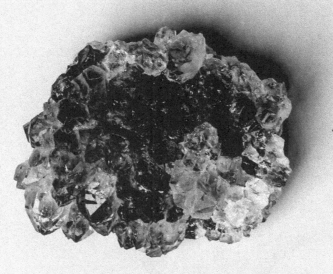

If you concentrate on finding whatever is
good in every situation, you will discover that
your life will suddenly be filled with gratitude,

a feeling that nurtures

the soul.

— **Harold Kushner**

Three things that happened today (or yesterday)
that I'm grateful for

Something in
my life
that I am grateful for

....
....
....
....
....
....

Something from
my past
that I am grateful for

....
....
....
....
....
....

One thing from
my future
that I *will* be grateful for

(something I am consciously creating and that I claim NOW) ....

....

....

....

....

....

....

....

....

....

....

....

....

....

....

One of my
eternal blessings

....

....

....

....

....

....

....

....

....

....

....

....

A single grateful thought
towards heaven
is the most
*perfect*prayer.

– Ephraim Gotthold Lessing

Three things that happened today (or yesterday) *that I'm grateful for*

Something in *my life* that I am grateful for

....
....
....
....
....
....

Something from *my past* that I am grateful for

....
....
....
....
....

One thing from
my future
that I *will* be grateful for

(something I am consciously creating and that I claim NOW) ....

....

....

....

....

....

....

....

....

....

....

....

....

....

....

One of my
eternal blessings

I am grateful that I can
heal, grow, and change.

With Divine Enthusiasm, I bless
all that I have and look with
wonder + gratitude
at their Abundant Increase.

-Catherine Ponder

Three things that happened today (or yesterday)

that I'm grateful for

Something in *my life* that I am grateful for

....
....
....
....
....
....

Something from *my past* that I am grateful for

....
....
....
....
....
....

One thing from
my future
that I *will* be grateful for

(something I am consciously creating and that I claim NOW) ....

....

....

....

....

....

....

....

....

....

....

....

....

One of my
eternal blessings

*wake at dawn
with a winged heart*
and give thanks for another
day of loving.

— Kahlil Gibran

Three things that happened today (or yesterday)

that I'm grateful for

Something in *my life* that I am grateful for

....
....
....
....
....
....

Something from *my past* that I am grateful for

....
....
....
....
....
....

One thing from
my future
that I *will* be grateful for

(something I am consciously creating and that I claim NOW) ....

....

....

....

....

....

....

....

....

....

....

....

....

....

One of my
eternal blessings

I cherish the idea that I am one with every person, plant, animal, substance, and essence in the universe.

Don't wait for your entire *ship to come in to feel grateful.*

Be grateful for every single nickel, every free meal, every perk and every discount that comes your way. Feeling gratitude for the abundance you have will give you more reasons to feel more gratitude.

- Boni Lonnsburry

Three things that happened today (or yesterday)

that I'm grateful for

Something in *my life* that I am grateful for

....

....

....

....

....

....

Something from *my past* that I am grateful for

....

....

....

....

....

....

One thing from
my future
that I *will* be grateful for

(something I am consciously creating and that I claim NOW) ....

....

....

....

....

....

....

....

....

....

....

....

....

....

One of my
eternal blessings

....

....

....

....

....

....

....

....

....

gratitude is the fairest blossom which springs from the soul.

– Henry Ward Beecher

Three things that happened today (or yesterday)
that I'm grateful for

....

....

....

....

....

....

....

....

....

....

....

....

....

Something in *my life* that I am grateful for

....

....

....

....

....

....

Something from *my past* that I am grateful for

....

....

....

....

....

....

One thing from
my future
that I *will* be grateful for

(something I am consciously creating and that I claim NOW) ....

....

....

....

....

....

....

....

....

....

....

....

....

....

One of my
eternal blessings

I know and love the fact that anything can be healed.

Saying *"thank you"* is more than good manners. *it's good spirituality.*

– Alfred Painter

Three things that happened today (or yesterday)
that I'm grateful for

Something in
my life
that I am grateful for

....
....
....
....
....
....

Something from
my past
that I am grateful for

....
....
....
....
....

One thing from
my future
that I *will* be grateful for

(something I am consciously creating and that I claim NOW) ....

....

....

....

....

....

....

....

....

....

....

....

....

....

One of my
eternal blessings

gratitude is *riches*
complaint is *poverty.*

-Doris Day

Three things that happened today (or yesterday)

that I'm grateful for

Something in *my life* that I am grateful for

....
....
....
....
....
....

Something from *my past* that I am grateful for

....
....
....
....
....
....

One thing from
my future
that I *will* be grateful for

(something I am consciously creating and that I claim NOW) ....

....

....

....

....

....

....

....

....

....

....

....

....

....

One of my
eternal blessings

I am thankful
for Divine grace.

Appreciation
is a wonderful thing.

It makes what is excellent in
others belong to us as well.

- Voltaire

Three things that happened today (or yesterday)

that I'm grateful for

Something in *my life* that I am grateful for

....
....
....
....
....
....

Something from *my past* that I am grateful for

....
....
....
....
....
....

One thing from
my future
that I *will* be grateful for

(something I am consciously creating and that I claim NOW) ....

....

....

....

....

....

....

....

....

....

....

....

....

....

....

One of my
eternal blessings

gratitude

is one of the sweet shortcuts
to finding peace of mind
& happiness inside.

No matter what is going on outside of us, there's always something we could be grateful for.

– Barry Neil Kaufman

Three things that happened today (or yesterday)
that I'm grateful for

....

....

....

....

....

....

....

....

....

....

....

....

....

....

Something in *my life* that I am grateful for

....
....
....
....
....
....

Something from *my past* that I am grateful for

....
....
....
....
....

One thing from
my future
that I *will* be grateful for

(something I am consciously creating and that I claim NOW) ....

....

....

....

....

....

....

....

....

....

....

....

....

....

One of my
eternal blessings

I'm happy that I don't need to figure out how to forgive—if I *intend* to forgive, I'll receive the guidance to make that happen.

TODAY
I AM
GRATEFUL

In our daily lives, we must see that it is not happiness *that makes us grateful,* but the gratefulness that makes us happy.

- Albert Clarke

Three things that happened today (or yesterday)

that I'm grateful for

Something in *my life* that I am grateful for

....
....
....
....
....
....

Something from *my past* that I am grateful for

....
....
....
....
....

One thing from
my future
that I *will* be grateful for

(something I am consciously creating and that I claim NOW) ....

One of my
eternal blessings

You cannot exercise much

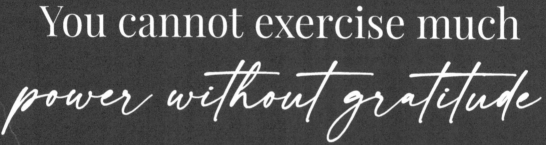

power without gratitude

*because it is gratitude that keeps you
connected with power.*

– Wallace Wattles

Three things that happened today (or yesterday)

that I'm grateful for

Something in *my life* that I am grateful for

....

....

....

....

....

....

Something from *my past* that I am grateful for

....

....

....

....

....

....

One thing from *my future* that I *will* be grateful for

(something I am consciously creating and that I claim NOW)

One of my
eternal blessings

I'm truly thankful that our physical world is an illusion and that we've been gifted the ability to create anything we desire in this illusion.

Counting blessings fills the
cells of the body *with health*
and the thoughts of the mind
—with love.

- Leiza Alpass

Three things that happened today (or yesterday)

that I'm grateful for

Something in *my life* that I am grateful for

....
....
....
....
....
....

Something from *my past* that I am grateful for

....
....
....
....
....
....

One thing from
my future
that I *will* be grateful for

(something I am consciously creating and that I claim NOW) ....

....

....

....

....

....

....

....

....

....

....

....

....

....

....

One of my
eternal blessings

Gratitude is a force born of *intimacy and compassion,*

giving birth to joy and beauty, growing into magical and mystical success and never ending happiness.

- Lazaris

Three things that happened today (or yesterday)
that I'm grateful for

Something in *my life* that I am grateful for

....

....

....

....

....

....

Something from *my past* that I am grateful for

....

....

....

....

....

....

One thing from
my future
that I *will* be grateful for

(something I am consciously creating and that I claim NOW) ....

....

....

....

....

....

....

....

....

....

....

....

....

....

One of my
eternal blessings

**I am grateful that love
changes everything.**

If the only prayer you said in your whole life was,

"Thank you"

that would suffice.

- Meister Eckhart

Three things that happened today (or yesterday)

that I'm grateful for

Something in *my life* that I am grateful for

....

....

....

....

....

....

Something from *my past* that I am grateful for

....

....

....

....

....

....

One thing from *my future* that I *will* be grateful for

(something I am consciously creating and that I claim NOW) ....

....

....

....

....

....

....

....

....

....

....

....

....

....

....

One of my
eternal blessings

We can only be said to be alive in those moments *when our hearts are conscious of our treasures.*

- Thornton Wilder

Three things that happened today (or yesterday)
that I'm grateful for

Something in *my life* that I am grateful for

....
....
....
....
....
....
....

Something from *my past* that I am grateful for

....
....
....
....
....
....

One thing from
my future
that I *will* be grateful for

(something I am consciously creating and that I claim NOW) ....

....

....

....

....

....

....

....

....

....

....

....

....

....

One of my

eternal blessings

I'm in love with the truth
that we are eternal.

Also by *Boni Lonnsburry*

THE COMPANION GUIDE TO
The Map: To Our Responsive Universe - Where Dreams Really Do Come True!
WINNER OF SEVEN INTERNATIONAL BOOK AWARDS

THE
Map
WORKBOOK

Contains **NEW BONUS MATERIAL** and sample Creation Sessions so you can start shifting your reality right now!

THE *Map* TO
ABUNDANCE
WORKBOOK

THE NO-EXCEPTIONS PLANNER
FOR CREATING MONEY,
SUCCESS, & BLISS

THE *Map*

TO OUR
RESPONSIVE
UNIVERSE—
WHERE DREAMS
REALLY DO
COME TRUE!

LIFE ON PLANET
EARTH
A USER'S MANUAL

WRITTEN BY THE PLANET EARTH WELCOMING
ENGLISH TRANSLATION BY
BONI LONNSBURRY

THE *Map* TO
ABUNDANCE

THE NO-EXCEPTIONS GUIDE
TO CREATING MONEY,
SUCCESS, & BLISS

MESSAGES
~ FROM YOUR ~
UNSEEN
FRIENDS
VOLUME TWO

MESSAGES
~ FROM YOUR ~
UNSEEN
FRIENDS

BONI LONNS

BONI LONNSBURRY

creation
JOURNAL

*A Magical Place to
Design Your Dreams*

Success
JOURNAL

*A Magical Place to
Record Your Triumphs*

Also by
Boni Lonnsburry

The Map: To Our Responsive Universe,
Where Dreams Really Do Come True!

The Map Workbook

The Map to Abundance: The No-Exceptions Guide
to Creating Money, Success, & Bliss

The Map to Abundance Workbook

Messages from Your Unseen Friends: Volume I

Messages from Your Unseen Friends: Volume II

Life on Planet Earth: A User's Guide (e-book)

Creation Journal: A Magical Place to Design Your Dreams

Success Journal: A Magical Place to Record Your Triumphs

All of Boni's books are available at:
www.LiveALifeYouLove.com/Shop

About the
author

Boni Lonnsburry is the Chief Visionary Officer of Inner Art Inc., an expert on conscious creation, and the author of ten books, including The Map: To Our Responsive Universe, Where Dreams Really Do Come True! and The Map to Abundance: The No-Exceptions Guide to Creating Money. Success, & Bliss, which together have won fifteen awards, including the Nautilus Award and the Silver Benjamin Franklin Award.

By applying the Universal Law of Attraction, Boni transformed her life of poverty, loneliness, and despair to one of abundance, love, and joy. She now teaches others to do the same.

**Learn more about Boni's work at
www.*LiveALifeYouLove.com* and *CreationSchool.com***